MW00877767

A Lamb Called Love

Author : Milly Bennitt

Illustrator : Bishoy Gendi

Editor : Shereen Tadros

Produced by Seraph Creative

A Lamb Called Love

Authors note

A Lamb called Love is a funky retelling of creation and the gospel.
I hope this book will break in pieces any thought that God can be confined
to a box of our understanding.

It was written following a vision that I had while living in Hong Kong. I was
filled with wonder at God's love and grace towards me and how that empowers
us to participate with heaven. This revelation sparked a desire to invite future
generations of world changers into the fun adventure of tangible relationship
with the Trinity, established in the security of knowing Love.

It has been great to work with Bishoy who has marvellously captured the
extravagance and wonder of the Trinity.

I hope you enjoy and participate in the adventure as you read,

Milly

A Lamb Called Love

Before time and hours and the stars above
Papa and Spirit were singing with Love

Although it was dark like the blackest night
Their beautiful chorus switched on the light.

Together they made the rivers and sky
The mountains and forests, the birds that fly

But Man was the only one who was like them
Papa's true masterpiece, Love's greatest gem.

They showed Man the beasts
     – the big and the small

With Papa beside him,
     he named them all.

Then, while he slept,
they made from his side

A Woman to love
– an equal; a bride.

Woman and Man were so happy and glad
Best friends with Papa, they never felt sad.

Then Snake came along and whispered his lie
He wanted Man and the Woman to die.

When they believed him,
they thought all was lost

But Love made things right
despite the great cost.

The Lamb we call Love died for you and me
To give us new hearts and new eyes to see.

Spirit breathed in Love   restored him to life

So we could be free

from sorrow and strife.

For Love tells the truth
and Love made a vow

So we could be with him
in Heaven now !

He sits with Papa
on a golden throne

Because he's with us,
we're never alone

But Snake keeps trying
to steal and to trick

He keeps telling lies
and makes people sick.

Love gave us power,
    now Snake has to flee

He's a weakling compared
    to you and me !

Love keeps in a bottle
your precious tears

He takes away worries
and chases fears.

Love is our King and our very best friend
The party's begun and will never end

All of the angels are dancing together
Singing a new song, laughing forever !

And still they are singing their happy song
A song that reminds us where we belong

A song so beautiful, merry and wild......

"Always remember,
I love you my child"

A Lamb Called Love

Milly Bennitt

Milly currently lives in the south of England. She has lived all over the world sharing the love of God.

Milly enjoys daily encounters with God in heaven and on the earth. She hopes to give children the inspiration to step into the reality of heaven. That they would feel empowered, loved by a fun God with an open invitation to experience Him in all His fullness and to grow in their journey walking in the ways of Love.

You can follow Milly and her journey at www.cabinacademy.com

Bishoy Gendi

Bishoy is an illustrator and animator living and working in London who loves to make stories and characters come to life. He has a gorgeous wife and three beautiful little girls.

You can follow Bishoy at www.bishoygendi.blogspot.com

Seraph Creative

Seraph Creative is a collective of artists, writers, theologians & illustrators who desire to see the body of Christ grow into full maturity, walking in their inheritance as Sons Of God on the Earth.

You can contact us or check out our latest resources at www.seraphcreative.org

Note from the Publisher:

"A Lamb Called Love" is quite a book. Received in a vision in Sai Kung, Hong Kong; completed in Sydney, Australia; illustrated in London, England; formatted on the Island of Patmos, Greece (of Revelations fame) and the ancient city of Smyrna, Turkey (also of Revelations fame), formatted for print in Cape Town, South Africa and finally converted to eBook in Arizona, USA.

It is a privilege to be involved with Milly and Bishoy and we hope to see much more. We know "A Lamb Called Love" will open you and your children even further to the Love and reality of the Trinity.

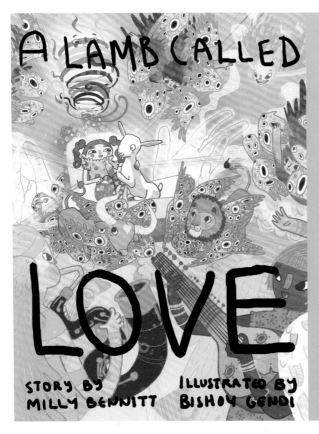